the dressing-up book

By Wendy Baker

Written and Edited by Diane James
Still-Life Photographs by Jon Barnes
Photographs of Children by Fiona Pragoff

Scholastic Canada Ltd
123 Newkirk Rd, Richmond Hill, Ontario, Canada

First published in Great Britain in 1990 by
Two-Can Publishing Ltd, 27 Cowper Street, London EC2A 4AP

Illustration and design © Wendy Baker, 1990
Text and compilation © Two-Can Publishing Ltd, 1990

ISBN 0–590–73871–2
87654321   Printed in Hong Kong   1234/9

Front cover photograph © Fiona Pragoff 1991

CONTENTS

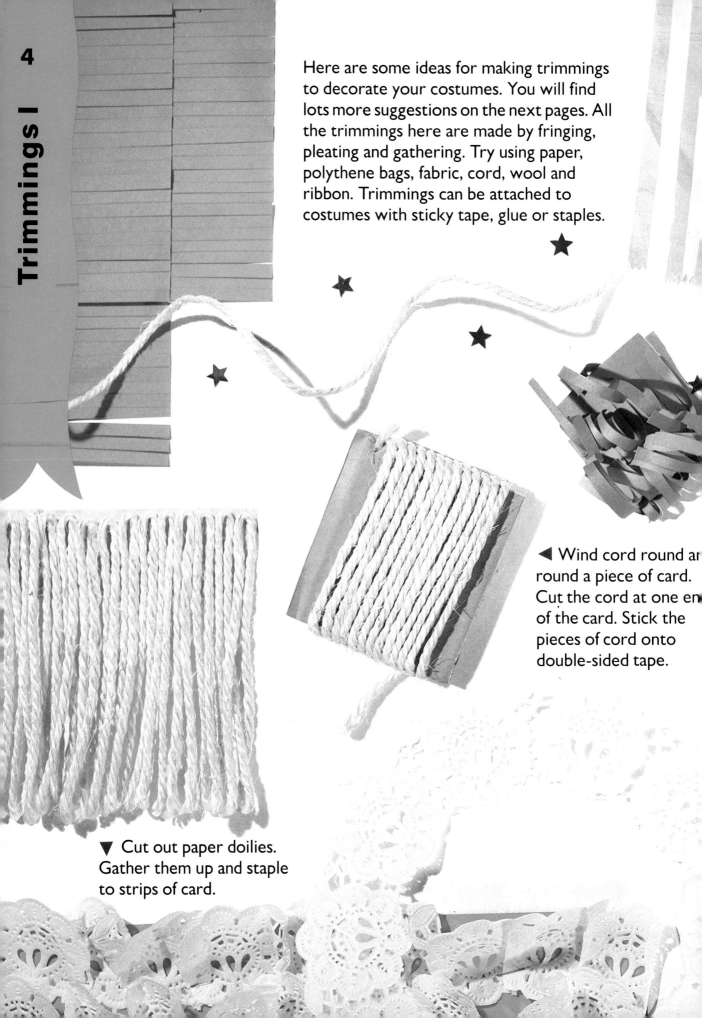

Here are some ideas for making trimmings to decorate your costumes. You will find lots more suggestions on the next pages. All the trimmings here are made by fringing, pleating and gathering. Try using paper, polythene bags, fabric, cord, wool and ribbon. Trimmings can be attached to costumes with sticky tape, glue or staples.

◄ Wind cord round and round a piece of card. Cut the cord at one end of the card. Stick the pieces of cord onto double-sided tape.

▼ Cut out paper doilies. Gather them up and staple to strips of card.

▼ Cut a square of fabric with a hole in the middle. Make a slit from the middle of one of the sides to the hole. Spread the fabric out and you will have a pointed fringe like the one below.

Flowers can change an ordinary costume into something really special. Make a good supply and turn them into garlands, head-dresses, bouquets and buttonholes!

Making Flowers

Cut a strip of fabric or paper, or some polythene from an old shopping bag. Starting at one end, wind the strip up. Secure the end with tape or staples.

You can make different flowers by fringing or cutting triangles in the strip before you wind it up. Another very simple method is to scrunch up lengths of soft tissue and secure the ends.

You can also make flowers by cutting out flat shapes and sticking them together like the one in the top corner. Try making leaves in the same way. Score down the centre of the leaves and fold gently.

You can make bows from fabric, polythene, tissue paper or crêpe paper. Cut a rectangular shape and pinch it together in the middle. Wind a thin strip of the same material round the middle and glue or staple it in place. You can decorate bows by sticking on coloured shapes or painting them.

Cut buckle shapes from card and decorate them with foil, glitter or beads. You can use buckles for belts or shoes.

Cut two identical circles from card with holes in the middle. Put one circle on top of the other. Wind wool round and round until the hole is nearly covered. Ask a grown-up to cut the wool between the pieces of card. Tie a length of wool round the pompon before taking the card away. Make tassels in a similar way using two rectangles of card. Cut the wool between the pieces of card at one end and tie a piece of wool around the uncut end of the tassel.

You can save a lot of time by making trimmings into long strips before attaching them to your costume. You can buy some trimmings by the metre in department stores. Or, you can make your own by threading flowers, bows, stars or silver balls (made from crumpled foil) on to thread. Make holes in the trimmings first and thread cord through by hand or use a needle and thread

You can buy special fabric fastener from department stores. It comes in various shapes and sizes but most kinds have a sticky back like double-sided tape. Tiny fibres on the fabric fastener cling to each other when you press two pieces together. You can use fabric fastener to fasten the backs of costumes by sticking down strips or by using button shapes. The fabric fastener will not show and it is easy to undo when you want to take the costume off!

You can use ribbon tied in a bow to ten cuffs, necklines and waists. Keep the bbon in place with double-sided tape.

Punch holes in fabric and lace together ith cord or ribbon. You can use this chnique to fasten the backs or fronts of stumes or belts.

Make buckles from thick card. Slot a rip of fabric through the buckle and sten back the end. Slot the other end of e strip through the buckle and out the her side. If you have any trouble, look at w an existing belt works.

Here are some ideas for decorating paper to use for trimmings or for costumes.

Pleat a sheet of paper and cut patterns in the folds. When you unfold the paper you will have a beautiful lace-like effect.

You can print on paper using objects such as sponges, building blocks or the ends of cardboard tubes. Or, you can make a potato print. Cut a potato in half and cut a pattern on one side. Cover the potato with thick paint and print on the paper.

A very quick way to decorate paper is to dip a thick paint brush into runny paint and flick it up and down the paper. It is best to do this outside as it can be very messy!

Padding

Many of the costumes in this book need some sort of padding to give them shape. You may want to make a skirt stick out, or to make shoulders look square.

Look out for padding material, such as newspapers, foam rubber, cardboard rolls and corrugated card.

To pad out a skirt, fold a large polythene bag in half and staple it at the sides and one end. Fill it with crumpled paper, staple the remaining end and attach it to the inside of the skirt at the waist. Foam rubber is particularly good for shoulder pads.

It is hard to believe that the beautiful ballgowns here were made from black polythene bags! They are decorated with flowers made from strips of coloured polythene. Find out how to make these ballgowns on the next page.

To make the boy's dress shirt, bow tie and lapels, cut shapes from black and white card similar to the ones below. The tabs at the neck of the shirt are used to attach the collar. Cut out a paper doily to decorate the shirt.

You will need about four large polythene bags to make a ballgown and it is easier to make it on the person it is for. Cut the bags open and staple into a long length for the skirt. Gather the waist and staple as you go along. Use double thickness strips for the top and pleat and staple into soft folds. Use strips of fabric fastener to fix the band at the back. You can staple the skirt to the top or use a wide sash to cover the join.

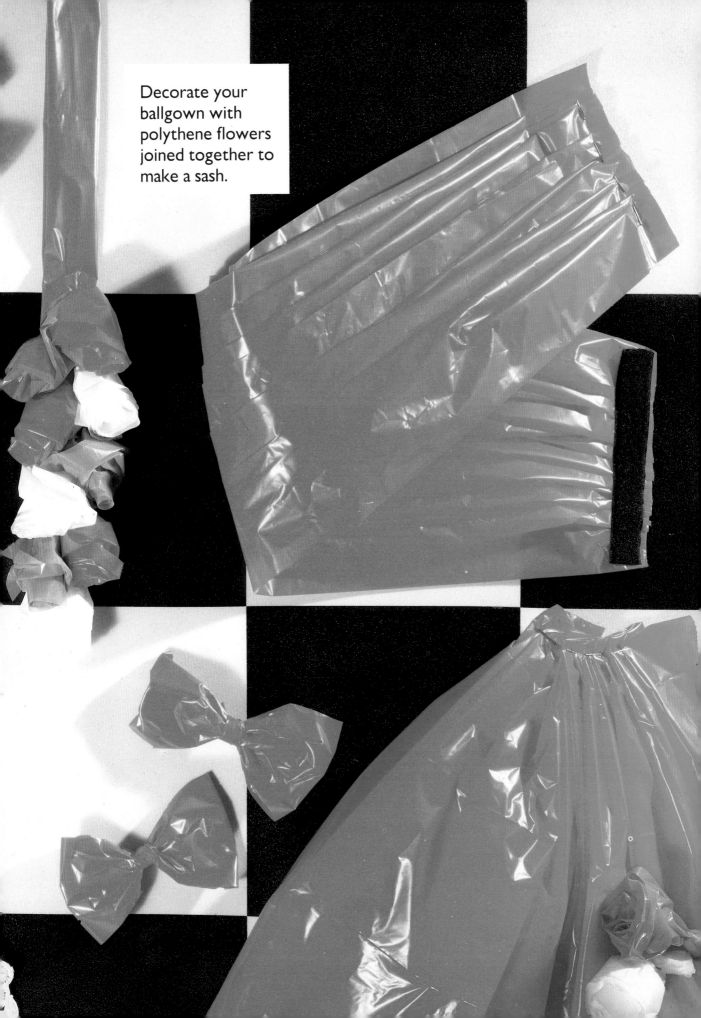

Decorate your ballgown with polythene flowers joined together to make a sash.

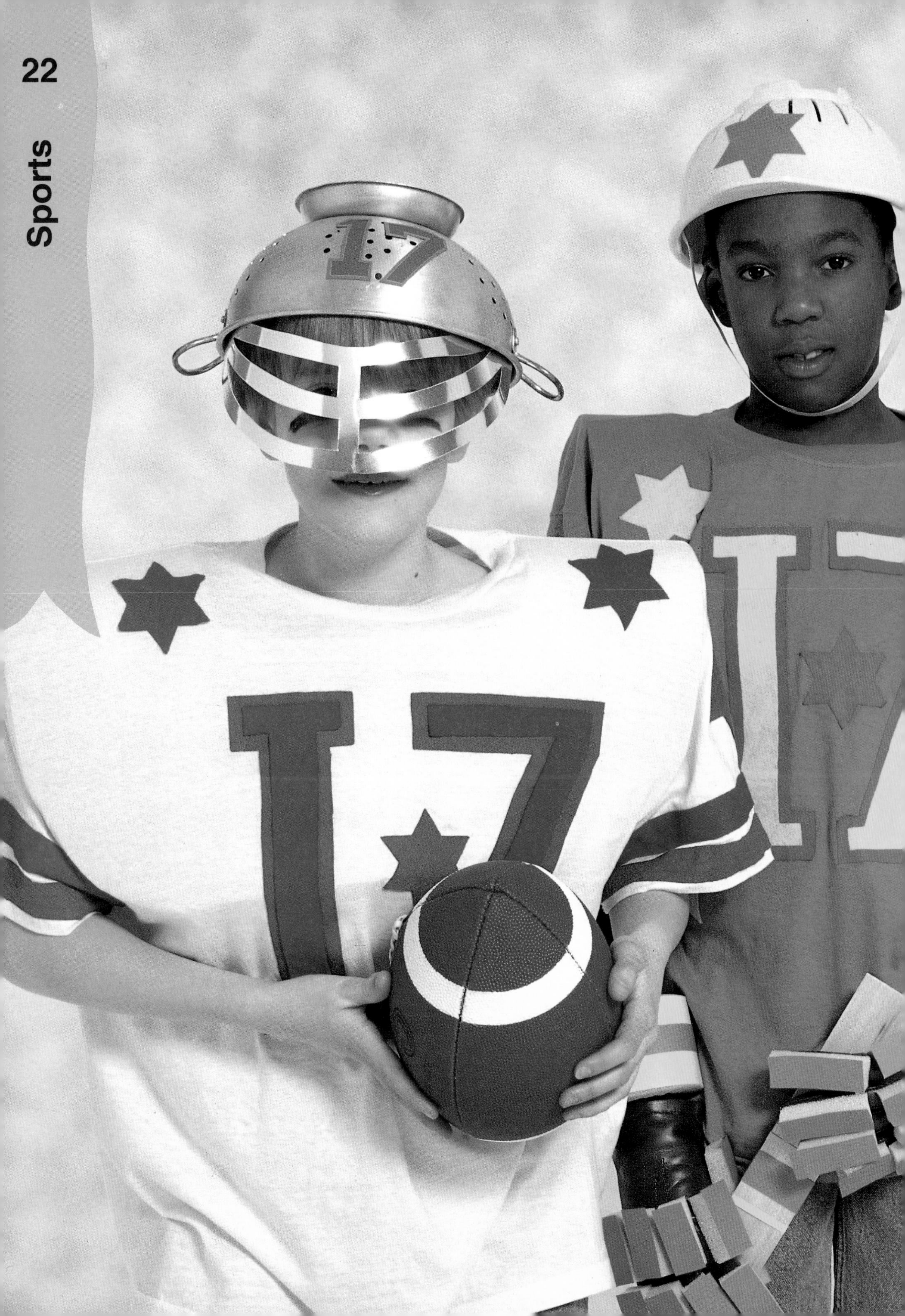
17
17

You do not need to buy expensive sports clothes to look the part! We made our football player's shirt by cutting letters and shapes from felt and gluing them on to a plain T-shirt. The shoulders are padded with pieces of foam. The helmet is a colander with a visor made from cardboard. The hockey player's shirt can be made the same way.

For the hockey player's padded gloves, cut pieces of foam rubber - you could use a sponge - and stick them on to a pair of old gloves. To make our cheerleader's skirt, cut circles out of red and white crepe paper. Gather the waist by pleating and stapling. Stick shapes to the waist band to cover the staples.

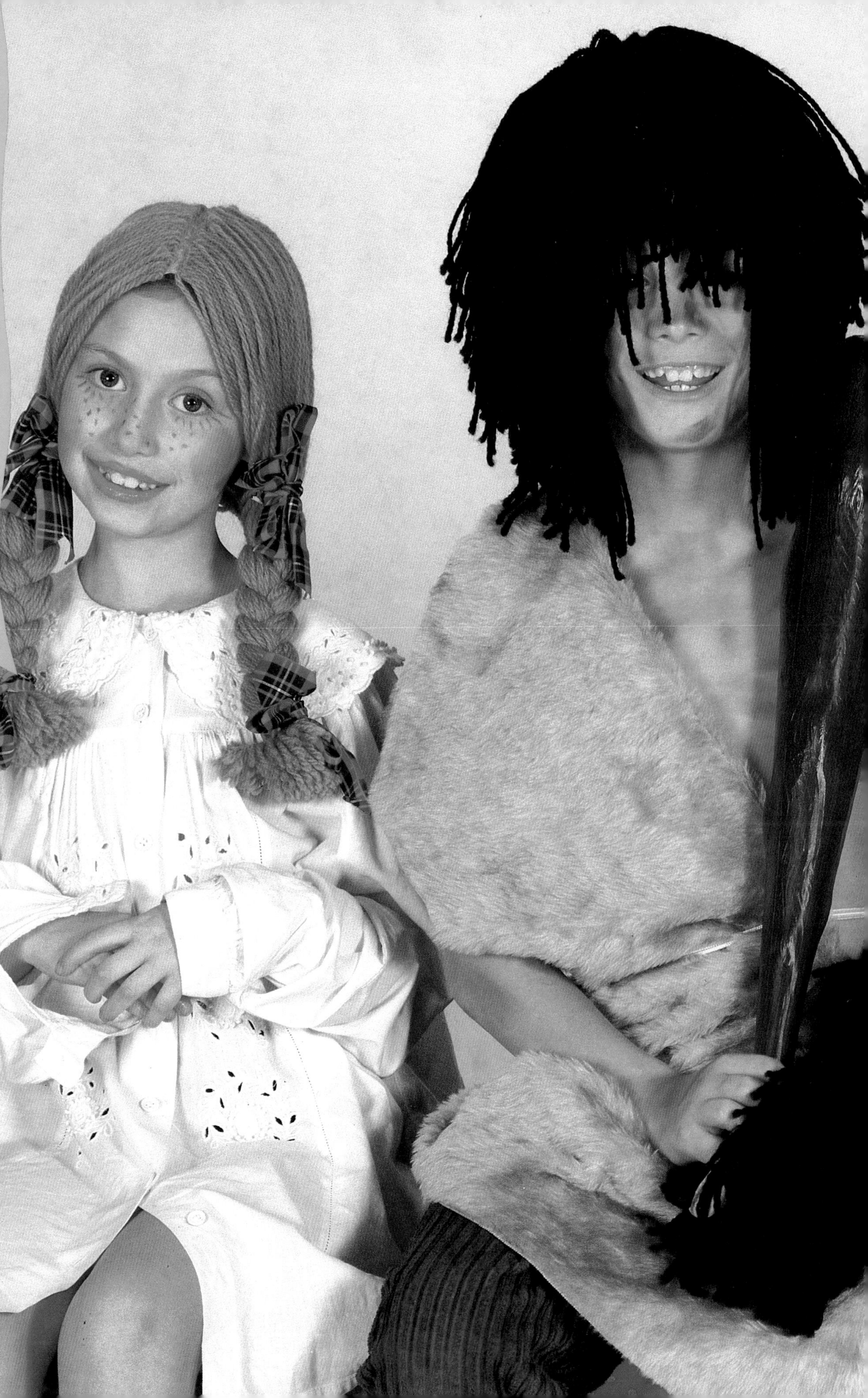

It is amazing how different someone can look with a completely new hair-style! A wig is easy to make and often adds the perfect finishing touch to a costume. Look at the next pages for some useful ideas.

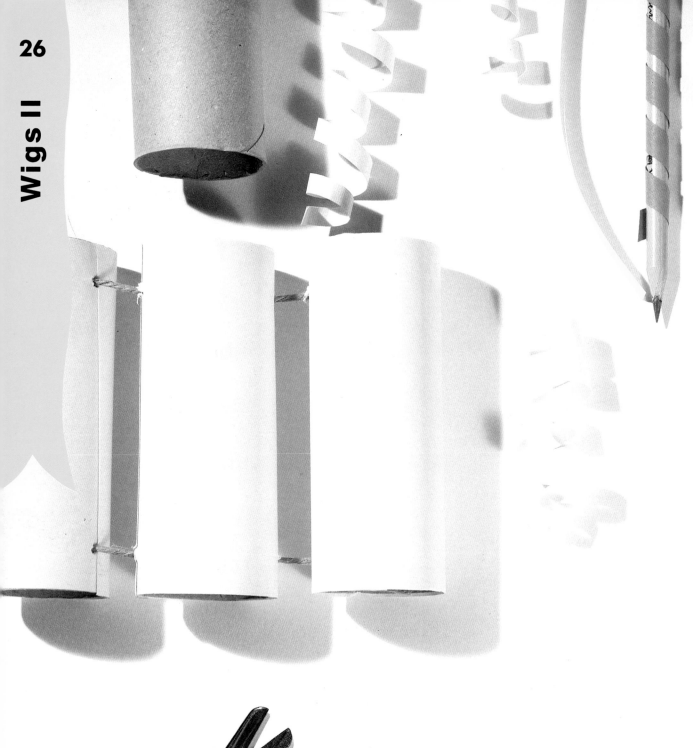

To make the judge's wig, cover cardboard rolls with white paper. Pierce holes at either end and thread string through. Make one strip of rolls to go over your head lengthways and attach the side pieces with sticky tape.

The clown's wig is made by sticking paper curls on to a swimming cap. Make sure the base is completely covered so that it does not show.

Stick long lengths of wool to a strip of sticky tape. You can then make plaits or pony tails, or you can cut the wool into uneven lengths to make a shaggy wig!

If you need inspiration for a costume, look at pictures of clothes that were worn in the past. The costumes here are based on clothes that were worn in Elizabethan times in England. Note details such as sleeves, necklines, colours and fabrics. Make belts, hats, gloves and jewellery to go with your costume.

We made our Elizabethan costumes from wallpaper with a raised pattern. This looks like the original material but is much less expensive! You could also use plain paper and decorate it (see page 14).

First we cut out the main shapes, such as the boy's trousers at the bottom of this page and the girl's bodice and skirt opposite. Try to keep these shapes as simple as possible. Start with a square or rectangle and cut out shapes for arms, legs and neck.

We made the lace trimming from pleated paper doilies and the beads and buckles using aluminum foil. The boy's ruff was made from two circles of card with a strip of pleated paper sandwiched between them.

It is best to fit the main pieces round the person who is going to wear the costume and then staple or tape in position.

Masks

Elephant Mask
Ask a grown-up to cut a length of wire and shape it over your head. Cut ears from card, fold them over the wire and glue in position. Make a separate trunk from card. Attach string or elastic at the sides to tie around your head.

Bird Mask
Make two holes in a paper plate so you can see out! Glue paper feathers to the plate. Make a beak from stiff paper and glue it on to the plate.

Monster Mask
This monster was made from a moulded plastic bottle. The nose is the handle of the bottle. Ask a grown-up to slit the bottle open opposite the handle and make holes to see through. Cover the bottle with foil. Pull the slit apart and the mask will grip firmly to your head.

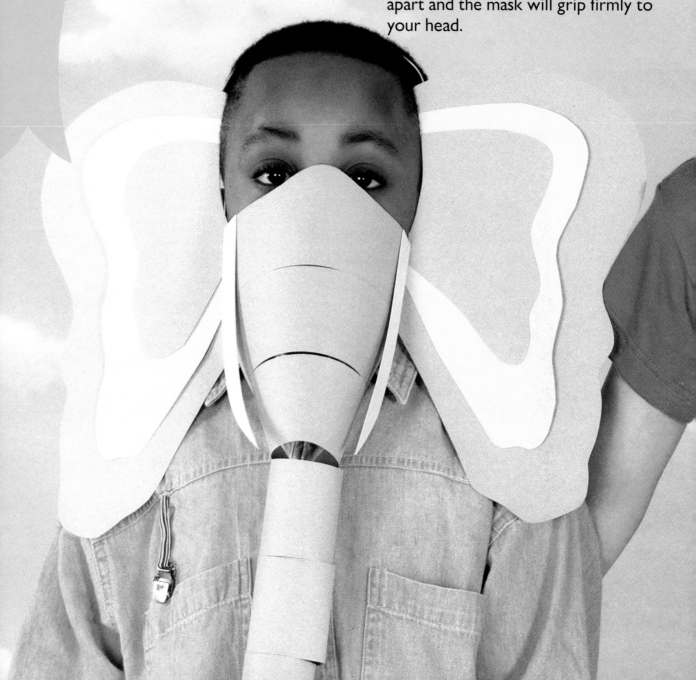

Knight & Sea Monster

To make the knight in shiny armour, we used moulded card taken from a fruit box, aluminum foil dishes and corrugated and plain card. You can either paint the card silver or cover it with aluminum foil. Look out for kitch equipment, like a vegetable strainer, which makes a perfect helmet!

Our sea monster's costume was made from strips of coloured polythene stapled to a base of clear polythene. You could also use net or paper strips. The monster's neck and shoulders were made by decorating paper plates stapled to the base. Look at page 32 to see how we made the monster's mask.

If you do not want to hide behind a mask, try making some colourful glasses to go with your costume. Use an old pair of glasses as a guide and cut out cardboard frames and side pieces. Stick on paper shapes, sequins or glitter. For a finishing touch, glue a sheet of coloured plastic to the back of the glasses. You could also bend a length of wire to make frames for a more serious pair of glasses!

To make our shiny cracker, we used a sheet of thin cardboard rolled into a tube shape and stapled at the back. The ruffles at the top and the bottom are made from pleated paper.

For the present, you will need a large cardboard box. Make a hole in the top and the bottom so it will slip easily over your head. Cover the box with coloured paper and add a giant bow. The valentine costume is simply two large hearts cut from cardboard and decorated around the edges with pleated doilies.

For all of the costumes, attach two strips of cardboard or wide tape at the top to put over your shoulders.

Don't forget your hands and feet when you are planning your costume! You can use fabric paints to decorate canvas shoes and replace laces with ribbons. Look at the trimmings pages at the beginning of the book and add pompons, fringes and bows to gloves and shoes. Or you could paint your feet and hands with body paint.

These costumes are best for sunny days! We made the grass skirt by sandwiching lengths of coarse string between two layers of strong tape. The top is a piece of flowered material knotted at the front.

You can knot sarongs – made from a rectangle of fabric – in all sorts of ways. Try experimenting in front of a mirror. Look at the instructions for making flowers from rolled up polythene at the front of the book.

Here are some really easy hats to put together quickly for a party. The exotic carnival hat is simply a scarf tied in a big knot with plastic fruit attached. The Indian head-dress is made from paper and the chef's hat is white paper pleated and taped on to a circle of white card. The pirate is wearing a scarf tied at the back.

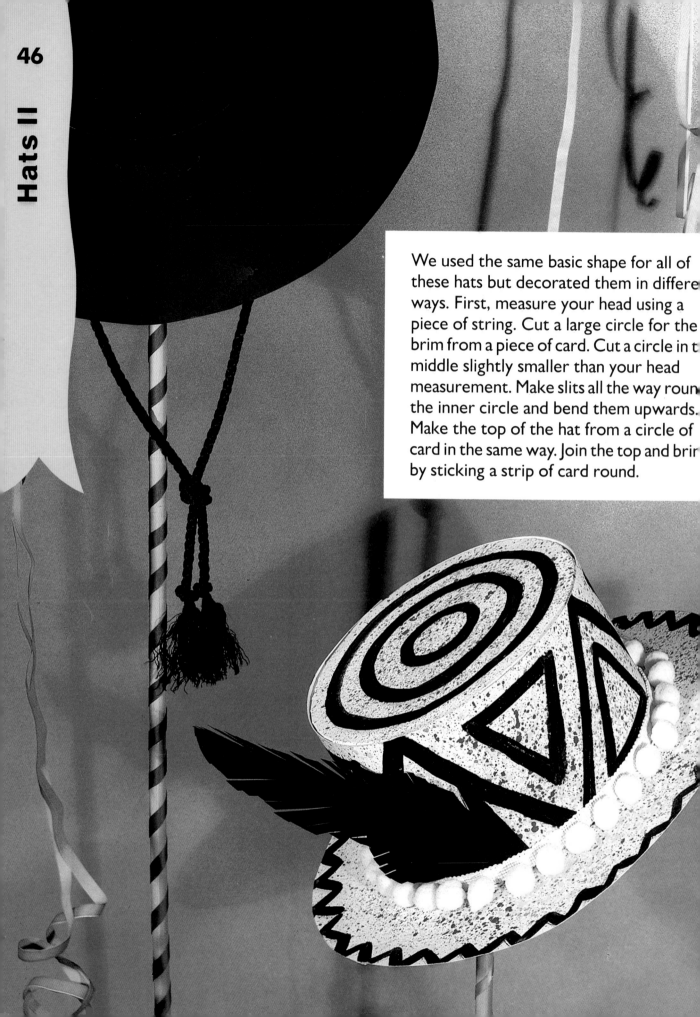

We used the same basic shape for all of these hats but decorated them in differe ways. First, measure your head using a piece of string. Cut a large circle for the brim from a piece of card. Cut a circle in t middle slightly smaller than your head measurement. Make slits all the way roun the inner circle and bend them upwards. Make the top of the hat from a circle of card in the same way. Join the top and brir by sticking a strip of card round.